The Nurse Journal

5-5-2021

HAPPY NURSES' WEEK!

Hope you find joy and inspiration in THE NURSE JOURNAL.

Rhoda R. Redulla

Rhoda Redulla, DNP, RN, NPD-BC

This nurse journal belongs to

_____

Honoring all nurses. This book
celebrates you!

To my family
(Tim, Tricia, & Noah), I see lots of
love & sunshine with you!

Table of Contents

This book is about you! Enjoy writing as you reminisce precious memories and wonderful accomplishments as a nurse. It includes writing prompts, inspiring quotes and fun facts about you. Soon or years from now, you could be sharing this journal with your family, friends, and fellow nurses. Created in the 2021 Year of the Nurse, may it bring warmth, joy, and fulfillment.

*"Nursing is an art:
and if it is to be an art,
it requires as exclusive a
devotion, as hard a
preparation, as any painter's
or sculptor's work; for what is
the having to do with dead
canvas or cold marble,
compared with having to do
with the living spirit-the
temple of God's spirit? It is one
of the Fine Arts; I had almost
said, the finest of the Fine
Arts."*

-Florence Nightingale

NURSING SCHOOL
What did you love most about nursing school?

_____
_____
_____
_____
_____
_____
_____
_____
_____
_____
_____
_____
_____
_____
_____
_____
_____

NURSING SCHOOL
What was your favorite class?
What did you like about it?

_____

_____

_____

_____

_____

_____

_____

_____

_____

_____

_____

_____

_____

_____

_____

_____

NURSING SCHOOL
What was your least favorite class?
What did you not like about it?

_____

_____

_____

_____

_____

_____

_____

_____

_____

_____

_____

_____

_____

_____

_____

_____

_____

_____

NURSING SCHOOL
*If you can go back in time,
what would you like to learn more about?
Or spend more time on?*

_____

_____

_____

_____

_____

_____

_____

_____

_____

_____

_____

_____

_____

_____

_____

_____

_____

NURSING SCHOOL
Share a special memory from your clinical practicum

_____

_____

_____

_____

_____

_____

_____

_____

_____

_____

_____

_____

_____

_____

_____

_____

_____

NURSING SCHOOL
What was the greatest challenge you had to overcome while in nursing school?

_____

_____

_____

_____

_____

_____

_____

_____

_____

_____

_____

_____

_____

_____

_____

_____

_____

NURSING SCHOOL
Who were your closest buddies?

_____

_____

_____

_____

_____

_____

_____

_____

_____

_____

_____

_____

_____

_____

_____

_____

_____

_____

_____

NURSING SCHOOL
What groups or clubs were you involved with?

_____

_____

_____

_____

_____

_____

_____

_____

_____

_____

_____

_____

_____

_____

_____

_____

_____

_____

_____

*"Do small things
with great love"*

- Mother Teresa

YOUR FIRST NURSING JOB
Where was your first job?

_____

_____

_____

_____

_____

_____

_____

_____

_____

_____

_____

_____

_____

_____

_____

_____

_____

YOUR FIRST NURSING JOB
Do you remember your first job interview?
What did you do to prepare for it?

_____

_____

_____

_____

_____

_____

_____

_____

_____

_____

_____

_____

_____

_____

_____

_____

_____

_____

YOUR FIRST NURSING JOB
Share an unforgettable memory

_____
_____
_____
_____
_____
_____
_____
_____
_____
_____
_____
_____
_____
_____
_____
_____
_____
_____
_____

YOUR FIRST NURSING JOB
What were your biggest fears as a new nurse?

_____

_____

_____

_____

_____

_____

_____

_____

_____

_____

_____

_____

_____

_____

_____

_____

_____

_____

YOUR FIRST NURSING JOB
What were your biggest and proudest moments as a new nurse?

_____

_____

_____

_____

_____

_____

_____

_____

_____

_____

_____

_____

_____

_____

_____

_____

YOUR FIRST NURSING JOB
Can you remember the first time you gave an injection? How was it?

YOUR FIRST NURSING JOB
What can you remember about your preceptor/s?

_____
_____
_____
_____
_____
_____
_____
_____
_____
_____
_____
_____
_____
_____
_____
_____
_____

YOUR FIRST NURSING JOB
How did you feel when you got your first pay check? Do you remember what you did with it?

_____

_____

_____

_____

_____

_____

_____

_____

_____

_____

_____

_____

_____

_____

_____

_____

"Do not go where the path may lead, go instead where there is no path and leave a trail."

-Ralph Waldo Emerson

YOUR NURSING CAREER
What made you pursue nursing?

_____

_____

_____

_____

_____

_____

_____

_____

_____

_____

_____

_____

_____

_____

_____

YOUR NURSING CAREER
Of all the jobs you've had, what is your favorite?

_____

_____

_____

_____

_____

_____

_____

_____

_____

_____

_____

_____

_____

_____

_____

_____

_____

YOUR NURSING CAREER
Describe your favorite boss.

_____
_____
_____
_____
_____
_____
_____
_____
_____
_____
_____
_____
_____
_____
_____
_____
_____
_____

YOUR NURSING CAREER
What do you love most about being a nurse?

_____

_____

_____

_____

_____

_____

_____

_____

_____

_____

_____

_____

_____

_____

_____

_____

_____

_____

"When you're a nurse, you know that every day you will touch a life or a life will touch yours."

— Anonymous.

YOUR NURSING CAREER
Was there a time when you almost gave up on nursing?

_____

_____

_____

_____

_____

_____

_____

_____

_____

_____

_____

_____

_____

_____

_____

_____

_____

YOUR NURSING CAREER
Share a special memory
during the COVID 19 pandemic

_____

_____

_____

_____

_____

_____

_____

_____

_____

_____

_____

_____

_____

_____

_____

_____

_____

_____

_____

YOU & YOUR PATIENTS
What are your personal values that guide you when caring for your patients?

_____

_____

_____

_____

_____

_____

_____

_____

_____

_____

_____

_____

_____

_____

_____

_____

YOU & YOUR PATIENTS
Which is the one patient you will not forget?
Why?

_____

_____

_____

_____

_____

_____

_____

_____

_____

_____

_____

_____

_____

_____

_____

_____

_____

_____

_____

YOU & YOUR PATIENTS
Can you share your experience caring for a dying patient?

_____

_____

_____

_____

_____

_____

_____

_____

_____

_____

_____

_____

_____

_____

_____

_____

YOU & YOUR PATIENTS
What has been an emotionally challenging
experience you had with
a patient and/or their family?

_____
_____
_____
_____
_____
_____
_____
_____
_____
_____
_____
_____
_____
_____
_____
_____
_____
_____
_____

YOU & YOUR PATIENTS

*What has been the most rewarding experience
you had with a patient and/or their family?*

_____

_____

_____

_____

_____

_____

_____

_____

_____

_____

_____

_____

_____

_____

_____

_____

_____

YOU & YOUR TEAM
Describe someone whom you would always love to work with. What has this person done for you?

_____

_____

_____

_____

_____

_____

_____

_____

_____

_____

_____

_____

_____

_____

_____

_____

YOU & YOUR TEAM
Share an experience when you felt your team was behind you.

"I attribute
my success to this:
I never gave or took an excuse."

- Florence Nightingale

GROWING AS A NURSE
Did you move to a new specialization or new job?
What made you do it?

_____

_____

_____

_____

_____

_____

_____

_____

_____

_____

_____

_____

_____

_____

_____

_____

_____

GROWING AS A NURSE
If you pursued an advanced degree, what prompted you to do it?

_____

_____

_____

_____

_____

_____

_____

_____

_____

_____

_____

_____

_____

_____

_____

_____

_____

_____

GROWING AS A NURSE
Are you involved in projects or organizations outside of your job? Describe this experience.

_____

_____

_____

_____

_____

_____

_____

_____

_____

_____

_____

_____

_____

_____

_____

_____

_____

_____

_____

_____

GROWING AS A NURSE
Who has been a great role model for you?.

GROWING AS A NURSE
*Have you done an oral presentation at
your job or in a conference?*

_____

_____

_____

_____

_____

_____

_____

_____

_____

_____

_____

_____

_____

_____

_____

_____

_____

_____

_____

GROWING AS A NURSE
Have you been involved in research?
Share your experience here.

_____

_____

_____

_____

_____

_____

_____

_____

_____

_____

_____

_____

_____

_____

_____

_____

_____

_____

GROWING AS A NURSE
Have you mentored other nurses?

_____

_____

_____

_____

_____

_____

_____

_____

_____

_____

_____

_____

_____

_____

_____

_____

_____

_____

_____

NURSES ARE

educators
innovators
clinicians
leaders
informaticians
counselors
entrepreneurs
scientists
care navigators
advocates
safety experts

... and many more

"To accomplish great things we must not only act, but also dream; not only plan, but also believe."

- Anatole France

ASPIRATIONS
What is your biggest dream?

_____

_____

_____

_____

_____

_____

_____

_____

_____

_____

_____

_____

_____

_____

_____

_____

_____

_____

_____

_____

ASPIRATIONS
If you had a magic wand,
what role would you be doing now as a nurse?

_____

_____

_____

_____

_____

_____

_____

_____

_____

_____

_____

_____

_____

_____

_____

_____

_____

_____

_____

ASPIRATIONS
What are your aspirations as a nurse or for nursing?

_____

_____

_____

_____

_____

_____

_____

_____

_____

_____

_____

_____

_____

_____

_____

_____

_____

ASPIRATIONS
What would you change about your nursing career?

_____

_____

_____

_____

_____

_____

_____

_____

_____

_____

_____

_____

_____

_____

_____

_____

_____

_____

ASPIRATIONS
If you can live anywhere, where would it be?

_____

_____

_____

_____

_____

_____

_____

_____

_____

_____

_____

_____

_____

_____

_____

_____

_____

ALL ABOUT YOU
Describe your early years.
Share a special memory from childhood.

_____

_____

_____

_____

_____

_____

_____

_____

_____

_____

_____

_____

_____

_____

_____

_____

_____

_____

ALL ABOUT YOU
What are your hobbies?
How do you spend your spare time?

_____

_____

_____

_____

_____

_____

_____

_____

_____

_____

_____

_____

_____

_____

_____

_____

_____

_____

ALL ABOUT YOU
What do you do for self-care?

_____

_____

_____

_____

_____

_____

_____

_____

_____

_____

_____

_____

_____

_____

_____

_____

_____

ALL ABOUT YOU
What are your greatest traits?

_____

_____

_____

_____

_____

_____

_____

_____

_____

_____

_____

_____

_____

_____

_____

_____

_____

_____

_____

ALL ABOUT YOU
What are your pet peeves?

_____

_____

_____

_____

_____

_____

_____

_____

_____

_____

_____

_____

_____

_____

_____

_____

_____

_____

ALL ABOUT YOU
What inspires you to give your best?

_____

_____

_____

_____

_____

_____

_____

_____

_____

_____

_____

_____

_____

_____

_____

_____

_____

Positive Affirmations

I am giving
I am caring
I am kind
I am determined
I am grateful
I am joyful
I am brilliant
I am strong

Courage

cour·age
strength in the face of pain
or grief.

Oxford Languages

COURAGE
Share a time when you fought for what you believed in.

_____

_____

_____

_____

_____

_____

_____

_____

_____

_____

_____

_____

_____

_____

_____

_____

_____

_____

_____

COURAGE
Share a time when you defended a colleague.

_____

_____

_____

_____

_____

_____

_____

_____

_____

_____

_____

_____

_____

_____

_____

_____

Resilience

re·sil·ience
the capacity to recover
quickly from difficulties;
toughness.

Oxford Languages

RESILIENCE
Think of a nursing colleague whom you admire for their resilience.

_____
_____
_____
_____
_____
_____
_____
_____
_____
_____
_____
_____
_____
_____
_____
_____
_____
_____

RESILIENCE
When have you shown utmost resilience?

_____

_____

_____

_____

_____

_____

_____

_____

_____

_____

_____

_____

_____

_____

_____

_____

_____

RESILIENCE
How did you cope with the COVID19 pandemic?
What made you show up to work each day?

_____

_____

_____

_____

_____

_____

_____

_____

_____

_____

_____

_____

_____

_____

_____

_____

Joy

joy
a feeling of great pleasure
and happiness.

JOY
What gives you joy?

_____

_____

_____

_____

_____

_____

_____

_____

_____

_____

_____

_____

_____

_____

_____

_____

_____

_____

_____

_____

JOY
Share some of your most joyful moments as a nurse.

_____

_____

_____

_____

_____

_____

_____

_____

_____

_____

_____

_____

_____

_____

_____

_____

_____

_____

JOY
*Share some of your most joyful moments
with friends and family.*

_____

_____

_____

_____

_____

_____

_____

_____

_____

_____

_____

_____

_____

_____

_____

_____

_____

_____

_____

JOY
Post photos of your most joyful moments with friends and family.

Joy

Draw things that give you joy

Gratitude

grat·i·tude
the quality of being thankful;
readiness to show appreciation
for and to return kindness.

Oxford Languages

GRATITUDE
What are you most thankful for?

_____

_____

_____

_____

_____

_____

_____

_____

_____

_____

_____

_____

_____

_____

_____

_____

_____

_____

GRATITUDE
Share instances when you received messages
of gratitude from your patients.

_____

_____

_____

_____

_____

_____

_____

_____

_____

_____

_____

_____

_____

_____

_____

_____

_____

GRATITUDE
Write a thank you note to someone whom you feel grateful for.

_____

_____

_____

_____

_____

_____

_____

_____

_____

_____

_____

_____

_____

_____

_____

_____

_____

_____

_____